READING
Triumphs

Mc Graw Hill **Macmillan McGraw-Hill**

RFB&D

learning through listening

Students with print disabilities may be eligible to obtain an accessible, audio version of the pupil edition of this textbook. Please call Recording for the Blind & Dyslexic at 1-800-221-4792 for complete information.

B

The McGraw·Hill Companies

Macmillan
McGraw-Hill

Published by Macmillan/McGraw-Hill, of McGraw-Hill Education, a division of
The McGraw-Hill Companies, Inc., Two Penn Plaza, New York, New York 10121.

Printed in the United States of America

ISBN 0-02-192016-8

6 7 8 9 071 09 08

READING
Triumphs

 Macmillan
McGraw-Hill

CONTENTS

Working with Words

Phonics

Read the words.

can	nap	pat
Pam	ran	Sam
sat	cat	tap

Words to Know

Read the words.

I	jump
and	not

Time to Read

Read the story.

Jump!

I jump and jump.
Cat can not jump.
Cat can nap!

Pam Ran

by Linda Ross
illustrated by Ann Iosa

Pam sat.

Pam ran.

Pam can jump.

Pam ran and ran.

Pam ran!

Comprehension Check

Retell

Retell the story.
Use the pictures.

Think About It

1. Where does the story take place?
2. Why is Pam happy at the end?

Write About It

What can Pam do?

Pam can _____.

Sam Can Nap

by Linda Ortiz

illustrated by Nancy Cote

Sam ran.

Sam sat.

Sam can nap.

I can not nap.

I can pat Sam!

Comprehension Check

Retell

Retell the story.
Use the pictures.

Think About It

1. Who is the story about?
2. Why does the boy smile at the end?

Write About It

Can Sam nap?

Sam can _____.

Working with Words

Phonics

Read the words.

at	can	bat
bam	cat	Nat
tag	Sam	Pam
hat	ran	am

Words to Know

Read the words.

go	too
yes	we

Time to Read

Read the story.

We Can Go!

I can go.
Can Cat go, too?
Yes, Cat can.
We can go!

Tag

by Beatrice Reynolds
illustrated by Hector Borlasca

Can Nan tag Mac?

Nan can tag Mac.

Can Mac tag Nan?

Go, Nan, go!

Yes! Mac can tag Nan.

Comprehension Check

Retell

Retell the story.
Use the pictures.

Think About It

1. Who got tagged first?
2. Why are Nan and Mac tired at the end?

Write About It

Can Mac tag Nan?

Mac can _____.

At Bat

by Sam Wilson
illustrated by Paige Billin-Frye

I am at bat.

Bam! I can bat.

Can Nat bat?

Nat can bat, too.

We can bat!

Comprehension Check

Retell

Retell the story.
Use the pictures.

Think About It

1. Who hit the ball first?
2. Who do you think will hit the ball after Nat?

Write About It

Can Nat bat?

Nat can _____.

Working with Words

Phonics

Read the words.

fit	dig	big
in	Jim	lick
can	quick	sit
bag	is	pig

Words to Know

Read the words.

play	the
run	be

Time to Read

Read the story.

Pig and Cat

Pig and Cat play.
Cat ran in the bag.
Can Pig run in, too?
Be quick, Pig!

Can Jim Fit?

by E.T. Low
illustrated by Brian Lies

Tim can run in.

Min can run in.

Kim can run in.

Can Jim fit?

Jim is in the hat!

Comprehension Check

Retell

Retell the story.
Use the pictures.

Think About It

1. Who ran in first?
2. Why did the animals run out of the hat?

Write About It

Who ran in the hat?

_____ ran in the hat.

Big Max

by Beth Lewis

illustrated by Neecy Twinem

Big Max can sit.

Big Max can dig.

Big Max can lick.

Big Max can play.

Big Max can be big!

Comprehension Check

Retell

Retell the story.
Use the pictures.

Think About It

1. What did Big Max do after he got a basket?
2. How is Big Max a pal?

Write About It

What can Big Max do?

Big Max _____.

Working with Words

Phonics

Read the words.

Brad	trip	drag
Fran	grab	sit
Gram	grin	trick
crab	six	drip

Words to Know

Read the words.

a	good
do	on

Time to Read

Read the story.

A Good Cat

Brad has a good cat.

Liz is his cat.

Liz can do a trick.

Liz can jump on his lap!

49

A Trip!

by Ed Reyes

illustrated by Jana Christy

Gram packs six bags.

Fran sits on a bag!

Fran sits on six bags.

Gram grins. Fran grins.

Fran and Gram can go!

Comprehension Check

Retell

Retell the story.
Use the pictures.

Think About It

1. Who is the story about?
2. Why does Fran sit on
   the bags?

Write About It

What can Fran do?

Fran can _____.

Cris the Crab

by Linda Ross

illustrated by Bernard Adnet

Cris can do tricks.

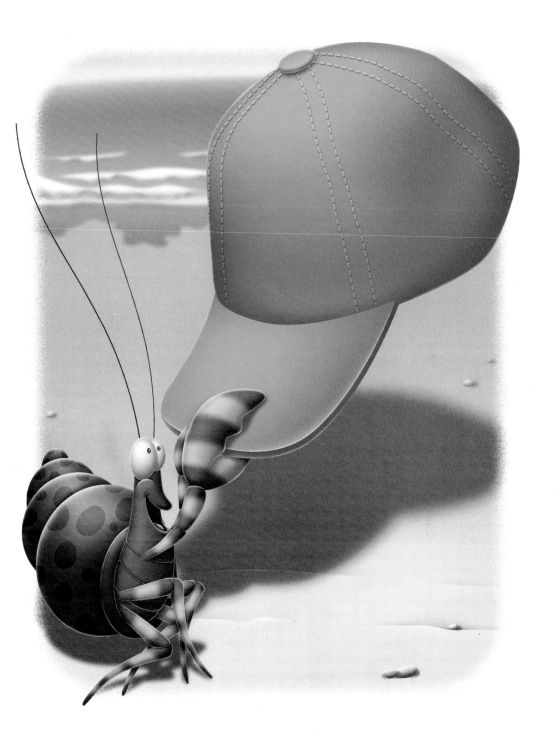

Cris can grab a cap.

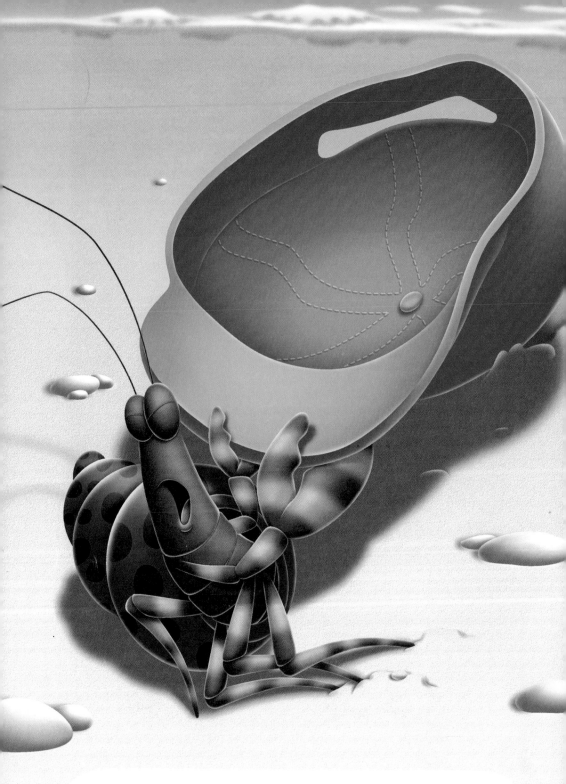

Cris can drag the cap.

Cris will nap in it.

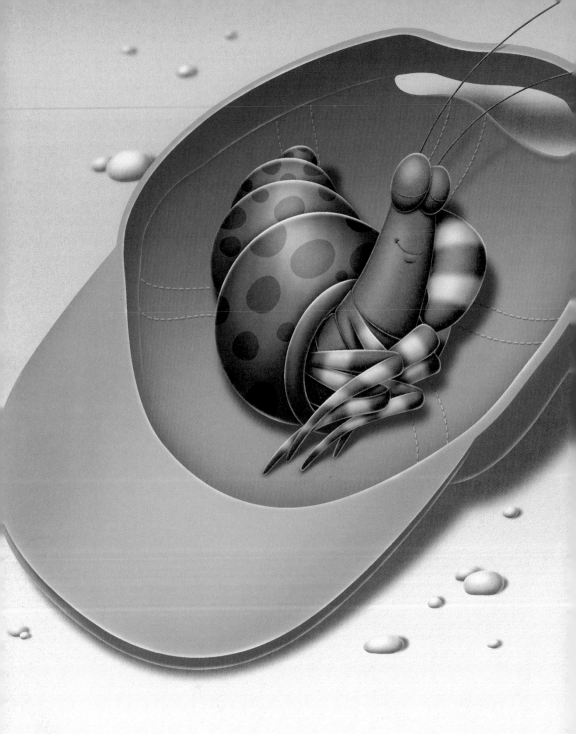

Good trick, Cris!

Comprehension Check

Retell

Retell the story.
Use the pictures.

Think About It

1. Where does the story take place?
2. What does Cris do with the cap?

Write About It

What can Cris do?

Cris can _____.

Working with Words

Phonics

Read the words.

and	sand	fast
hand	Hank	last
trip	ant	sink
drag	pink	list

Words to Know

Read the words.

little	what
help	very

Time to Read

Read the story.

Little Hank

Hank is a little pig.
What can Hank do?
Hank can help his dad.
Hank can fix a sink.
Hank is very good!

63

Big Cats

by Beatrice Reynolds

What can a big cat do?

It can run very fast.

It can sit and sip.

It can lick and lick.

It can nap at last.

Comprehension Check

Retell

Retell the story.
Use the pictures.

Think About It

1. Why did the author write about big cats?
2. What else do you think a big cat can do?

Write About It

What can a big cat do?

A big cat _____.

Ants, Ants, Ants!

by Linda Ross

What is in the hill?

Ants, ants, and ants!

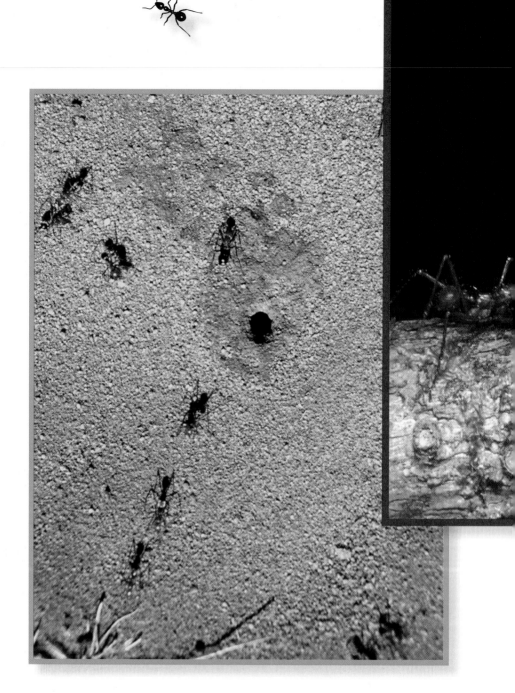

Ants can dig in sand.

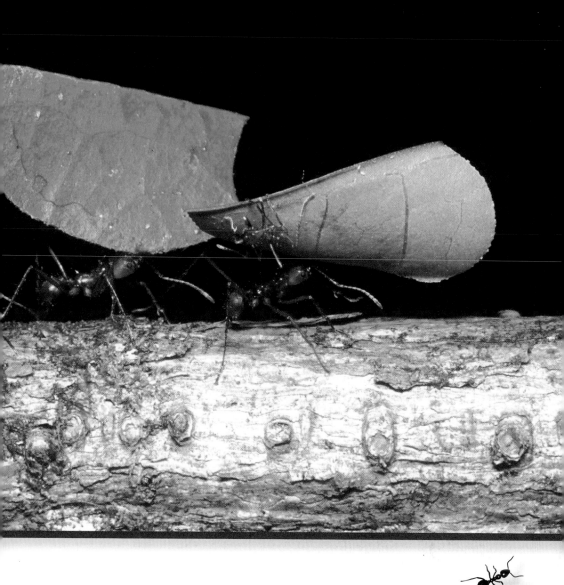

Little ants can help.

Ants can drag it back!

Comprehension Check

Retell

Retell the story.
Use the pictures.

Think About It

1. Why did the author write about ants?

2. How do ants help each other?

Write About It

What can ants do?

Ants can _____.

Working with Words

Phonics

Read the words.

hop	pond	frog
sing	jog	rock
on	dog	mom
top	trot	fast

Words to Know

Read the words.

my	her
see	they

Time to Read

Read the story.

Jill and Bob

My pal Jill has a dog.
Her dog is Bob.
I see Jill and Bob jog.
They can run fast.
See Jill and Bob go!

Hop, Frog, Hop!

by Lana Rios

See the frogs.

They can hop, hop, hop!

Frogs can hop in a pond.

Frogs can sit on pads.

Frogs can hop on a rock.

They can sit on top!

Comprehension Check

Retell

Retell the story.
Use the pictures.

Think About It

1. What is the story about?
2. What does a frog look like?

Write About It

What can frogs do?
Write a sentence.

My Mom

by Linda Ross

My mom is big.
I can sit on her lap.

My mom can hop fast.
Hop, hop, hop!

My mom can trot.
Trot, trot, trot!

Mom and I sip.

My mom can sing!

Comprehension Check

Retell

Retell the story.
Use the pictures.

Think About It

1. What is the story about?
2. Think of a mom. What can that mom do?

Write About It

What can a mom do?
Write a sentence.

Working with Words

Phonics

Read the words.

pet	leg	get
help	hop	fell
bed	red	pot
vet	well	Ken

Words to Know

Read the words.

who	no
look	are

Time to Read

Read the story.

Ken Gets a Pet

Who will get a pet?
Ken has no pets yet.
Look at the cats!
They are tan and red.
Ken picks a red cat!

Jen Helps Rex

by Beth Lewis

illustrated by Lizi Boyd

Who is Jen?
Jen is a vet.

Jen can help pets.

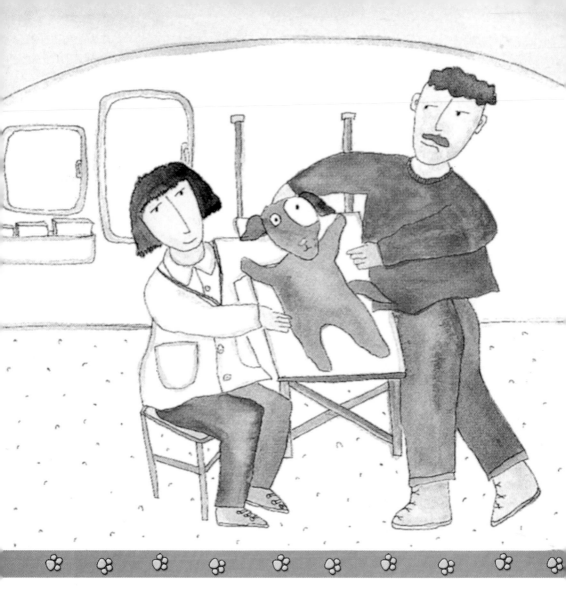

See Ben and Rex.
They are at the vet.

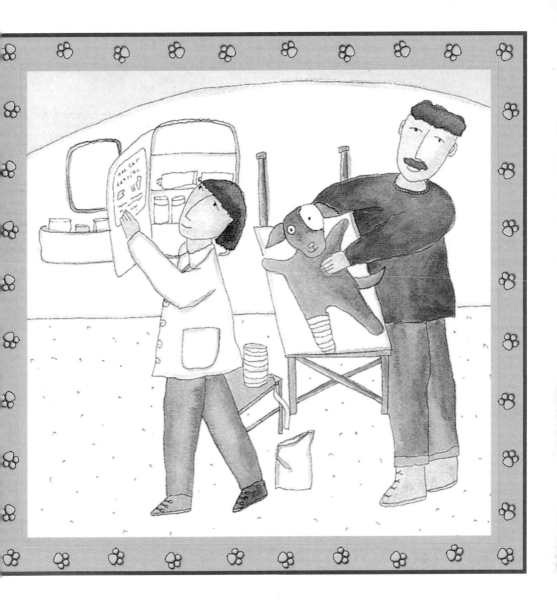

Rex has a bad leg.

Jen can fix Rex.
Rex will get well!

Comprehension Check

Retell

Retell the story.
Use the pictures.

Think About It

1. What does Jen do to help Rex?
2. Why do people take their pets to a vet?

Write About It

What do vets do?

On the Bed

by Keith Malcom
illustrated by Ken Spengler

Look at the bed!
Who can get on?

Ned can get on.
Ted can get on.

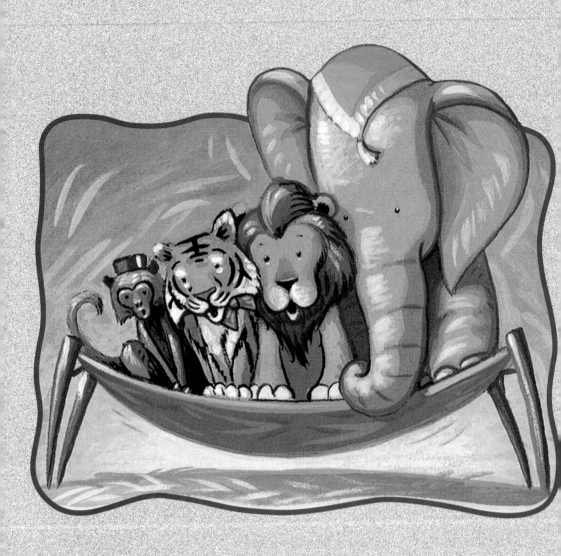

Dan can get on.
Nan can get on.

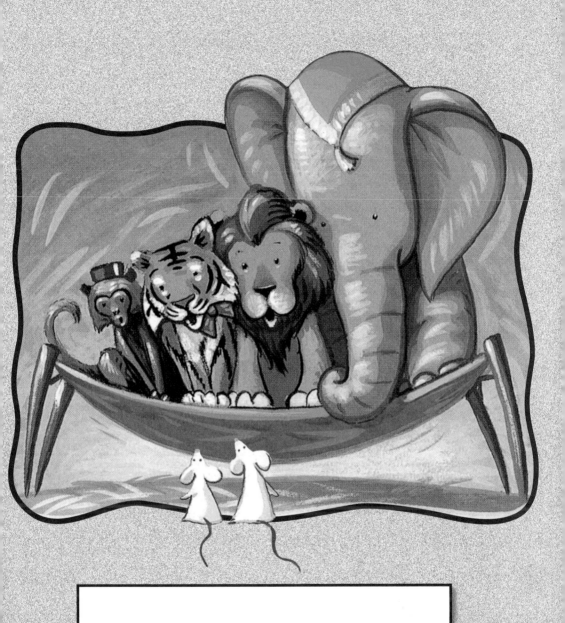

Can Jen get on?
Can Ben get on?

No! Look!
The bed fell.

Comprehension Check

Retell

Retell the story.
Use the pictures.

Think About It

1. Who got on the bed first?

2. Why did the bed fall down?

Write About It

What happened to the bed?

Working with Words

Phonics

Read the words.

ship	fish	shell
Beth	red	shop
that	them	thin
hen	thing	this

Words to Know

Read the words.

live	here
many	for

Time to Read

Read the story.

Fun on a Ship

Pip and Pep are cats.
They live on this ship.
They run and play here.
They go on many trips.
It is fun for them!

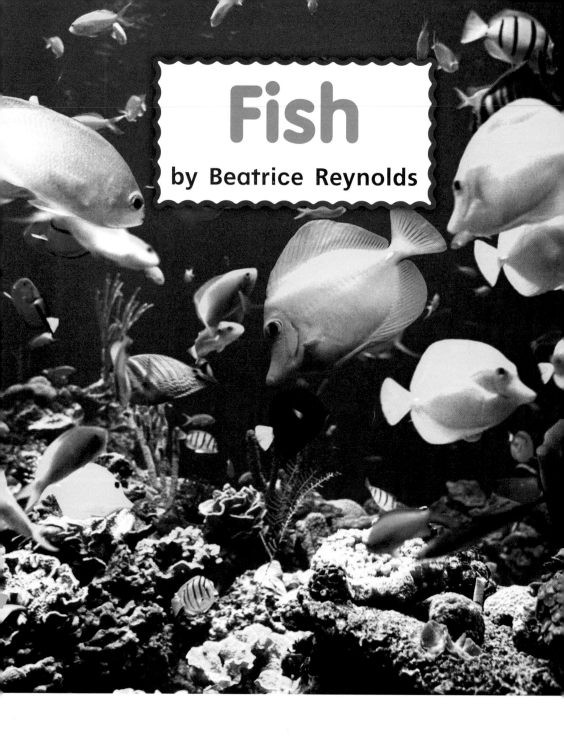

Fish

by Beatrice Reynolds

Fish live here.

fish has dots.

Fish can be fat.
Fish can be thin.

This fish is big.
It has big fins, too.

This fish is big.
This fish can go fast!

Comprehension Check

Retell

Retell the story.
Use the pictures.

Think About It

1. What kinds of fish are there?
2. Where do fish live?

Write About It

Write about a fish.
Tell what it looks like.

At the Shop

by Andy Hsu
illustrated by David Sheldon

Beth and Jon shop.
Mom helps them.

Beth gets a red ship.
Jon gets tan logs.

Beth gets many rocks.
Jon gets big shells.

They got many things.

The things are for fish!

Comprehension Check

Retell

Retell the story.
Use the pictures.

Think About It

1. What do Beth and Jon get at the shop?
2. How would you take care of fish?

Write About It

What other things go in a fish tank?

Working with Words

Phonics

Read the words.

Bud	pup	fun
run	fish	hug
jump	mud	drum
that	tub	up

Words to Know

Read the words.

to	want
make	have

Time to Read

Read the story.

The Jumping Pup

I run to the pet shop.
I want to get a pup.
Pups make good pets.
See that tan pup jump!
Can I have that pup?

Fun with Drums

by Linda Ross
illustrated by Kathi Ember

Gus has a pot.

Gus can make a drum.

Kim has a pan.
Kim can make a drum.

Gus and Kim have cans.
Gus and Kim can tap.

Gus and Kim have fun.

Gus and Kim can drum!

Comprehension Check

Retell

Retell the story.
Use the pictures.

Think About It

1. What is the first thing Gus uses as a drum?
2. What other things can be used as a drum?

Write About It

What can Gus and
Kim do?

Big Bud

by Vanessa Parks
illustrated by Don Madden

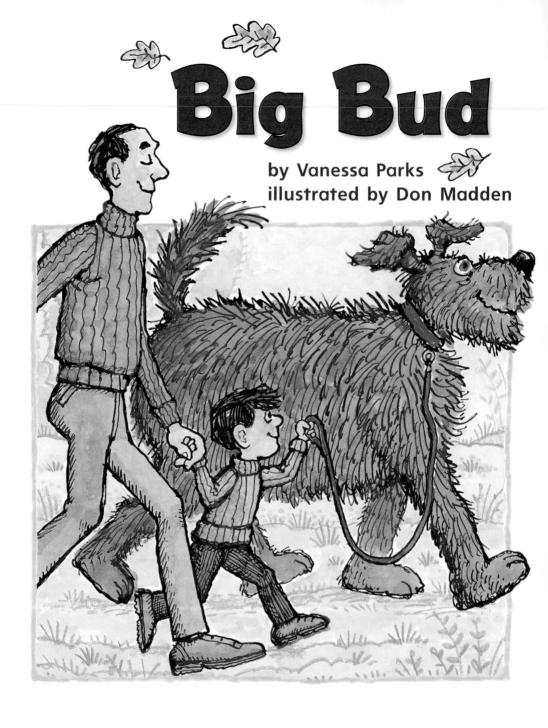

This is my dog, Bud.
Bud is big!

Bud can run fast.
Bud runs in the mud!

I fill up the tub.
Will Bud want to get in?

Yes! Bud gets in.

I want to hug Bud.
Bud is the best dog!

Comprehension Check

Retell

Retell the story.
Use the pictures.

Think About It

1. What happens after Bud runs in the mud?
2. Do you think Bud is a good dog? Why?

Write About It

What can Bud do?

Working with Words

Phonics

Read the words.

clank	bug	clap
flip	clip	clop
clink	slop	drum
plop	slip	plip

Words to Know

Read the words.

me	today
away	you

Time to Read

Read the story.

Play with Me

Play with me today!
Do not go away.
I can clap with you.
You can flip with me.
Let's clap and flip today!

Can You Clap?

by Beatrice Reynolds
illustrated by Kathleen Kemly

Can you clap and clap?
We can clap and clap!

Can you tap, tap, tap?
Let's tap, tap, tap!

Can you clip and clop?
We can clip and clop!

Can you jump and hop?
Let's jump and hop!

Can you run away?
We can run and play!

Comprehension Check

Retell

Retell the story.
Use the pictures.

Think About It

1. What do the children do after they clap?
2. What other things could the leader do?

Write About It

What games do you play with your friends?

Plip, Plop!

by Tina Edwards
illustrated by Liza Woodruff

It is wet today.
Plip, plop! Plip, plop!

Let's get a big pot.
Clink, clank, clink!

Let's mop it up.
Slip, slop! Slip, slop!

Hop with me.
Hip, hop! Hip, hop!

It is wet today.
We can play and play!

Comprehension Check

Retell

Retell the story.
Use the pictures.

Think About It

1. What happens after the monkeys mop?
2. How do the monkeys feel at the end?

Write About It

How did the monkeys solve their problem?

Skills and Strategies

TITLE	PHONICS	HIGH-FREQUENCY WORDS	COMPREHENSION
Vol.1 Unit 1 pages 6–75			
8 Pam Ran 14 Sam Can Nap	/a/ a c<u>a</u>n	and I jump not	Analyze Story Structure: Character and Setting
22 Tag 28 At Bat	/a/ a b<u>a</u>t	go too we yes	Analyze Story Structure: Character and Setting
36 Can Jim Fit? 42 Big Max	/i/ i d<u>i</u>g	be play run the	Analyze Story Structure: Sequence
50 A Trip! 56 Cris the Crab	/kr/ cr <u>cr</u>ab, /dr/ dr <u>dr</u>ag, /gr/ gr <u>gr</u>in, /tr/ tr <u>tr</u>ick	a do good on	Analyze Story Structure: Character and Setting
64 Big Cats 70 Ants, Ants, Ants!	/nd/ nd ha<u>nd</u>, /nt/ nt a<u>nt</u>, /st/ st fa<u>st</u>, /nk/ nk si<u>nk</u>	help little very what	Analyze Text Structure: Author's Purpose
Vol.1 Unit 2 pages 76–145			
78 Hop, Frog, Hop! 84 My Mom	/o/ o h<u>o</u>p	her my see they	Summarize: Main Idea and Details
92 Jen Helps Rex 98 On the Bed	/e/ e b<u>e</u>d	are look no who	Summarize: Retell
106 Fish 112 At the Shop	/sh/ sh <u>sh</u>op, fi<u>sh</u> /th/ th <u>th</u>in, Be<u>th</u>	for here live many	Summarize: Retell
120 Fun with Drums 126 Big Bud	/u/ u f<u>u</u>n	have make to want	Visualize: Sequence
134 Can You Clap? 140 Plip, Plop!	/kl/ cl <u>cl</u>ap, /fl/ fl flip, /pl/ pl <u>pl</u>op, /sl/ sl <u>sl</u>ip	away me today you	Visualize: Sequence
Vol.2 Unit 3 pages 6–75			
8 Dave and Kate 14 Jake's Cake	/ā/ a_e make	all eat said walk	Analyze Story Structure: Character and Setting
22 Snakes, Snakes, Snakes! 28 Kids Can Play	/sk/ sc <u>sc</u>ales, /sk/ sk <u>sk</u>ate, /sl/ sl <u>sl</u>ed, /sn/ sn <u>sn</u>ake, /sp/ sp <u>sp</u>in	together under was when	Analyze Text Structure: Main Idea and Details
36 Wake Up, Chicks! 42 Let's Eat Lunch	/ch/ ch <u>ch</u>ick, bun<u>ch</u>, /ch/ tch ca<u>tch</u>, /hw/ wh <u>wh</u>en	come our some your	Summarize: Retell
50 Five Ducks and a Frog 56 Miss White's Dime	/ī/ i_e d<u>i</u>me	how now there where	Generate Questions: Make Predictions
64 Stripes, Stripes, Stripes! 70 It's Spring!	/skr/ scr <u>scr</u>atch, /spl/ spl <u>spl</u>ash, /spr/ spr <u>spr</u>ing, /str/ str <u>str</u>ipes	three give of put	Generate Questions: Compare and Contrast

TITLE	PHONICS	HIGH-FREQUENCY WORDS	COMPREHENSION
Vol.2 Unit 4 pages 76–125			
78 Mole's Home	/ō/ o_e ho<u>le</u>	he into saw soon	Monitor Comprehension: Make Inferences
88 June's Flute	/ū/ u_e m<u>ule</u>, fl<u>ute</u>	could new she work	Monitor Comprehension: Draw Conclusions
98 Trains, Trains, Trains!	/ā/ ay d<u>ay</u>, ai s<u>ai</u>l	about know read these	Monitor Comprehension: Compare and Contrast
108 Let's Plant Seeds	/ē/ e b<u>e</u>, ee tr<u>ee</u>, ea p<u>ea</u>ch	after by down kind	Summarize: Main Idea and Details
118 Milly Cleans Up	/ē/ y happ<u>y</u>	before done pull two	Summarize: Beginning, Middle, and End
Vol.2 Unit 5 pages 126–175			
128 Three Billy Goats	/ō/ o g<u>o</u>, oa g<u>oa</u>t, ow sh<u>ow</u>	always over their try	Visualize: Fantasy and Reality
138 The Light	/ī/ ind k<u>ind</u>, y tr<u>y</u>, igh h<u>igh</u>	every fall never out	Visualize: Problem and Solution
148 At the Big Park	/är/ ar p<u>ar</u>t	any better or were	Generate Questions: Make Inferences
158 Fun with Sports	/ôr/ or sp<u>or</u>t	again around because great	Generate Questions: Cause and Effect
168 Birds' Nests	/ûr/ er h<u>er</u>, ir b<u>ir</u>d, ur f<u>ur</u>	does from warm would	Generate Questions: Classify and Categorize
Vol.2 Unit 6 pages 176–225			
178 Jack and the Beans	/ou/ ou c<u>ou</u>nt, ow n<u>ow</u>	been buy once upon	Summarize: Cause and Effect
188 A Good Birthday	/ů/ oo b<u>oo</u>k	laugh only small write	Monitor Comprehension: Make Predictions
198 The Sun and the Moon	/ü/ oo m<u>oo</u>n	blue call full one	Summarize: Compare and Contrast
208 Paws and Claws	/ô/ au f<u>au</u>lt, aw p<u>aw</u>s	carry four goes wash	Monitor Comprehension: Classify and Categorize
218 Toys at Night	/oi/ oi n<u>oi</u>se, oy t<u>oy</u>	eight open pretty seven	Monitor Comprehension: Use Illustrations

ACKNOWLEDGMENTS

ILLUSTRATIONS

7-12: Ann Iosa. 14-18: Nancy Cote. 21: Paige Billin-Frye. 22-26: Hector Borlasca. 28-32: Paige Billin-Frye. 35-40: Brian Lies. 42-46: Nancy Twinem. 49-54: Jana Christy. 56-60: Bernard Adnet. 63: Nancy Twinem. 77: Stacy Schuett. 91: Stacy Schuett. 92-96: Lizi Boyd. 98-102: Ken Spengler. 105: Carol Schwartz. 112-116: David Sheldon. 119: Carol Schwartz. 120-124: Kathi Ember. 126-130: Don Madden. 133: Liza Woodruff. 134-138: Kathleen Kemly. 140-144: Liza Woodruff.

PHOTOGRAPHY

All photographs are by Macmillan/McGraw Hill (MMH) except as noted below:

4: Tom Brakefield/CORBIS; 5: Dynamic Graphics Group/Creatas/Alamy; 64-65: (t) Winfried Wisniewski/Getty Images; 65: (b) Mike Hill/Alamy; 66: Clem Haagner/Gallo Images/CORBIS; 67: Tom Brakefield/CORBIS; 68: Charlotte Thamo/Alamy; 70: © plainpicture/Alamy; 71: Charlotte Thege/Peter Arnold, Inc.; 72: Jacob Halaska/Index Stock; 73: ALAN WATSON/WWI/Peter Arnold, Inc.; 74: Morales/Age Fotostock; 78: Wim Weenink/Foto Natura/Minden Pictures; 79: Masterfile (Royalty-Free Division); 80: Stephen Dalton/Animals Animals; 81: Jonathan Plant/Alamy; 82: Michael Gadomski/AnimalsAnimals; 84: Holger Ehlers/Alamy; 85: © Charles Philip Cangialosi/CORBIS; 86-87: S. Sebald/DEPL/Alamy; 87: © John Warden/AlaskaStock.com; 88: Norbert Rosing/National Geographic/Getty Images; 106: Carlos Davila/SuperStock; 107: Tom Brakefield/Bruce Coleman/PictureQuest; 108: Dynamic Graphics Group/Creatas/Alamy; 109: David Fleetham/Alamy; 110: Walt Sterans/Stephen Frink Collection/Alamy.